D0293305

You feel bad because you're in a vicious circle

The way you feel is affected by things that happen to you. Like the bad things on the opposite page. Those things are all outside of you. Sometimes, you can change what's happening outside, but often, you can't do much about them.

And when you allow them to affect your mood, the vicious circle kicks in and you feel worse and worse and worse…

Turn over to see how it works

First, an outside event affects you

When something happens, you naturally notice it and think about it. If you forget your sister's birthday, for example, you may think "I'm useless!"
This is called **Altered Thinking.**

Altered thinking can set off a chain reaction inside you that affects the way you feel and what you do.

When your altered thinking is negative (like "I'm useless"), the vicious circle is triggered and you can end up really down, not getting out of bed and even feeling ill. Let's watch the vicious circle in action.

Let's watch the
Vicious Circle in action

5

Altered thinking leads to altered feelings

If you think "I'm useless!" you're going to feel pretty low, sad or guilty.

Maybe you feel as if you've let her down, or you might feel guilty because you know you should have been more organised.

Altered feelings lead to altered physical symptoms

When you feel low or guilty, you can get sweaty, tense with stomach ache or headaches. Sometimes you can feel really tired.

Your hands might feel clammy, or you get an attack of the jitters and can't sit still.

Ever had a sinking feeling or felt your heart racing? It's probably that old vicious circle spinning round!

Altered physical symptoms lead to altered behaviour

It's only natural. You're really tired, you have a headache or maybe feel tense so you don't feel like going out, or even getting up. You steer clear of people who might ask if you sent a card or present. You stay in and hardly do any exercise. You're not eating right and you seem to catch all the bugs that are going round.

You might finish up at the doctor's, asking why you can't seem to shake off this virus you've had for weeks.

And you know what happens then? The circle goes round again, only this time, you're already ill, staying in bed and fed up, so you get even worse.

Vicious, these vicious circles, aren't they?

Now for the *good* news!

YOU
CAN
STOP
THE
CIRCLE!

You know the great thing about circles? They turn both ways!

In the same way that just one thing (an altered thought) led to everything else getting worse, you can start to make it better by changing one thing.

Just by eating differently or doing more exercise, or changing the way you think about some things, you can affect ALL THE OTHER THINGS IN THE CIRCLE and start to feel better.

Sounds too easy? Turn over for an example.

How to stop
the circle

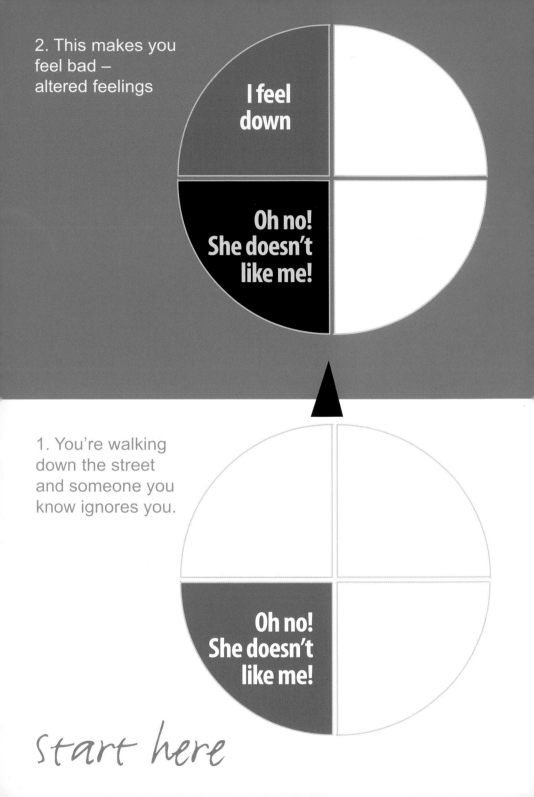

2. This makes you feel bad – altered feelings

I feel down

Oh no! She doesn't like me!

1. You're walking down the street and someone you know ignores you.

Oh no! She doesn't like me!

start here

3. You go home and avoid other people's company – altered behaviour

I feel down

I don't want to see anyone at the moment

Oh no! She doesn't like me!

4. You have no energy and maybe can't sleep that night for worrying about what happened – altered physical symptoms

I feel down

I don't want to see anyone at the moment

Oh no! She doesn't like me!

What's wrong with me? I feel tired and shattered

Now lets stop the circle!

2. You're concerned, so you run after her and ask her what's wrong

Is there anything I can do?

Poor Louise, she must be upset, I wonder what's wrong?

1. You're walking down the street and someone you know ignores you.

Poor Louise, she must be upset, I wonder what's wrong?

start here.

3. Louise explains and you listen like a good friend

Is there anything I can do?

I feel good about myself because I'm helping someone else

Poor Louise, she must be upset, I wonder what's wrong?

4. You arrange to see Louise later and discuss practical things you can do to help

Is there anything I can do?

I feel good about myself because I'm helping someone else

Poor Louise, she must be upset, I wonder what's wrong?

I feel really great, alert and strong

See how it works?

YOU HAVE CONTROL

You can take control and stop the vicious circle by changing just one thing – your thinking, your diet, your activities – almost anything. And it doesn't have to be a big thing!

You could start by changing the way you eat. By going out just one time. By doing just a bit more exercise. By changing the way you think about things.

If you manage to do something about just one thing, you'll break the vicious circle, stop it spinning down and down and start to feel better straight away.

Try it now! Good Luck

Look out for more books like this

Understanding the vicious circle is the key to taking control of how you feel.

Here are some more books that are based on the same ideas. They can all help you deal with different stuff and start to feel better.

You can get them from www.fiveareas.com

hope you find this book helpful, its not intended to be a direct substitute for
advice with a healthcare professional, nor do we give any assurances about
ess in a particular case.
neither the publisher nor the author shall be held liable for any loss or
ising from its use.

Dr Chris Williams,

www.livinglifetothefull.com

A Realspeak production
Published by Five Areas

Copyright © Dr C Williams (2007). All rights reserved.
First Published (2007). ISBN 978-1-906564-01-8

Further copies available from www.fiveareas.com (admin@fiveareas.com)

Living Life to the Full series

ISBN: 978-1-906564-01-8

9 781906 564018